ABC

Franklin Watts Incorporated

Brian Wildsmith

© Brian Wildsmith 1962

First published 1962 by Oxford University Press

First American publication 1963 by Franklin Watts, Inc.
575 Lexington Avenue, New York, N.Y. 10022

Library of Congress Catalog Card Number: 63 — 7131

Brian Wildsmith's ABC, a child's passport to the world of letters, ranks high not only with small children but with expert judges—librarians, reviewers, teachers. In the United States it has been chosen by the American Library Association for its list of Outstanding Books of 1963; by the New York Public Library for exhibit and listing in its 1963 booklet, *Children's Books Suggested as Holiday Gifts*; and by *The New York Times Book Review's* "Ten Best Illustrated Books of 1963." It has also been specially exhibited by the Library of Congress.

In Great Britain in 1963, the Kate Greenaway Award, comparable to the Caldecott Medal in the United States, was given to *Brian Wildsmith's ABC*.

Printed in the USA
by the Polygraphic Company of America

apple

APPLE

butterfly

BUTTERFLY

cat

CAT

dog

DOG

elephant

ELEPHANT

fish

FISH

goat

GOAT

horse

HORSE

iguana

IGUANA

jaguar

JAGUAR

kettle

KETTLE

lion

LION

mouse

MOUSE

nest

NEST

owl

OWL

peacock

PEACOCK

queen

QUEEN

rooster

ROOSTER

snail

SNAIL

turtle

TURTLE

unicorn

UNICORN

violin

VIOLIN

windmill

WINDMILL

xylophone

XYLOPHONE

yak

YAK

zebra

ZEBRA

A is for apple.	N is for nest.
B is for butterfly.	O is for owl.
C is for cat.	P is for peacock.
D is for dog.	Q is for queen.
E is for elephant.	R is for rooster.
F is for fish.	S is for snail.
G is for goat.	T is for turtle.
H is for horse.	U is for unicorn.
I is for iguana.	V is for violin.
J is for jaguar.	W is for windmill.
K is for kettle.	X is for xylophone.
L is for lion.	Y is for yak.
M is for mouse.	Z is for zebra.